Rush Hour

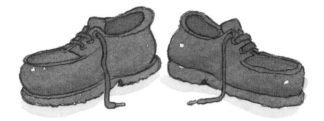

Paul Shipton

Illustrated by Jeffrey Reid

RIGBY

"I can't find my books.
Where are they?" asked Dad.

"There they are, on the chair," I said.

"Now I can't find my sandwiches.
Where are they?" asked Dad.

4

"Here they are, in the fridge," I said.

"Where are my keys?"
asked Dad.

"Here they are, on the
table," I said.

"Now I'm late. Where are my bags?" asked Dad.

"In the cupboard, Dad," I said.

"Where are my gloves?"
asked Dad.

"Oh Dad! They are in the drawer," I said.

"Where can my pens be?"
asked Dad.

"In your pocket," I said.

"Oh no! My glasses?" said Dad.

"On your head," I said.